Footk
Killers

Jonny Zucker

Illustrated by Pete Smith

Titles in the Full Flight Fear and Fun series

Badger Publishing Limited
Oldmedow Road,
Hardwick Industrial Estate,
King's Lynn PE30 4JJ
Telephone: 01438 791037
www.badgerlearning.co.uk   4 6 8 10 9 7 5

Football Killers   ISBN 978 1 84691 122 4

Series Editor: Jonny Zucker
Publisher: David Jamieson
Commissioning Editor: Carrie Lewis
Editor: Paul Martin
Design: Fiona Grant
Illustration: Pete Smith (Beehive Illustration)

Football
Killers

Contents

Badger
L E A R N I N G

1. Training

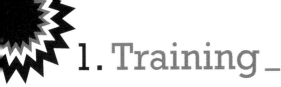

Two teams are joint top of the inter-galactic football league. Earth team, Sector 5, and Crust City from Planet Shine 21. There is one game left of the season – Crust City v Sector 5. The winners will come top of the league.

But Crust City, led by their evil captain, Fixer, are playing dirty. When they play, their opponents get very ill and some have even died! No one knows why this is happening.

Crust City are not using guns or bombs or missiles. No one can prove they are cheats. So no one can stop them!

Sector 5 captain, Dane Sky, wants to know what's going on.

We must beat Crust City on Saturday.

It's not possible.

They'll smash us and we'll die!

3. We will all die!

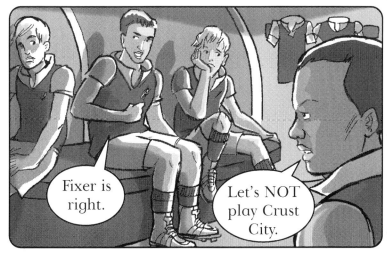

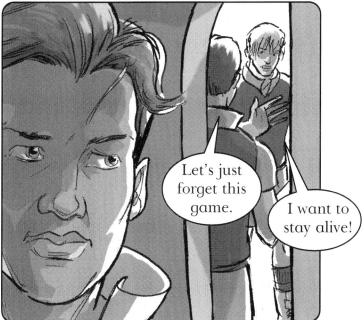

4. Space dash

I have to do this.

Finally, I can find out what they're up to.

There's nothing weird here.

CRUST CITY

CHANGING ROOM

Maybe I'll find something inside their changing room.

5. Trapped!

Aaaarrrrhhhh. My head hurts.

6. Last chance

It was the night before the big match at the Sector 5 stadium.

Twenty minutes later.

7. Match day

It's the day of the big match.

8. The final kick

Crust City scored first...

...but Sector 5 pulled one back.

Yes! 2-1 to us!

The game is over. Sector 5 have won!

I knew we could do it!